THE TWO WEEK WAIT CHALLENGE:

A SASSY GIRL'S GUIDE TO SURVIVING THE TWW

A CHALLENGE BY LINDSAY FISCHER

Printed in the United States of America

First Printing, 2016

ISBN: 978-0-9977433-0-2

Blonde & Always Write, Inc.
www.survivorswillbeheard.com

FORWARD

I was convinced I'd never worry about having children when I left my abusive partner because, quite honestly, I was never going to date again.

Time is a funny thing; it has proven me wrong over and over. I've learned from all my pledges that began with "I'll never" or "No way" that just when I'm certain something is bound to happen, the exact opposite of what I expect likes to show up and say, "Hey chick, what's up?" So imagine my surprise when three years after I left my abuser and while I was still enrolled in trauma therapy, I met the love of my life: a man so kind and unapologetic in his own feelings he made me want to be a better human right away. I could see myself having his babies long before we talked about that as a possibility. After all, if I was willing to risk everything by putting myself back out into the dating scene, I needed it to be for a worthwhile reason.

No more games. No more unnecessary heartache. We were going to do this right.

I worked hard to overcome my PTSD so we could make our relationship work. My therapist used the phrase "self-care" as if it were a condiment to pour on everything. Any action or inaction on my part meant I needed to focus more on my self-care.

"I'm feeling anxious," I said.

What did you do for self-care? she'd reply.

"I think I want to change career paths."

And your self-care?

"My mom is getting married in June and I need to find a dress that fits. I've lost so much weight through this depression I look like I pooped myself in every outfit."

But tell me how you're going to practice self-care while you shop for this new dress...

I should have expected that three years after I began therapy with her, one of her final pleas before I graduated from treatment would be about self-care:

Lindsay, tell me how you're going to continue using self-care when I'm not here to remind you of it anymore.

In truth, I didn't need her reminders by that point. She'd helped me overcome all the many medical acronyms that come with surviving domestic violence. I'd met other amazing survivors and written about this journey. Not only this but one month before my final session with her, I married my husband (the man who made my knees weak for all the right reasons). On Ka'anapali Beach in Maui, in front of our closest family members, we were married in a small beach ceremony, celebrating our new beginning at a luau reception.

At 30 years old I *knew* my time to conceive was dwindling and we just *had* to start trying to conceive on our honeymoon. I realize now how laughable this fear was because at that point I didn't need to know about ovulation calendars or kits and I didn't concern myself with follicles or trigger shots. All I knew was that in July of 2014 I'd go buy the super cute onesie I found at Target, the one with *Aloha, Mommy* embroidered in script across the chest, complete with a baby pineapple down below.

Of course that didn't happen.

It didn't happen the next month or the month after that. After six months of trying without a single big, fat positive (BFP) I decided it was time to start looking into causes for pregnancy complications.

I wasn't ready to call it infertility.

That's when my entire world started to revolve around the things I previously had the luxury of ignoring. I charted; I checked cervical mucus; I tracked my basal body temperature and used ovulation strips. For a while this helped me feel empowered and my dear husband liked how eager I was at various times of the month.

But as our journey continued I became more rigid in my rule following.

We couldn't have sex for three days before I was supposed to ovulate and once I had a positive test we'd baby dance (read: do the nasty) for the three days following. Of course, there were rules and regulations on when and how we could try conceiving. Masturbation for him, pre-ovulation, was a no-no (so his boys could bulk up and create the strongest swimmers). It was all science, no passion. And it totally sucked.

Fortunately, we already had 15 months of documentation on this journey by the time I got in to see my OB. He was ready to move forward with testing and see WTF was going on down there. In a bittersweet moment for us, we found out making a baby would be more complicated than a few rounds of baby dancing.

1. The sexual trauma I endured *might* have caused a slight injury to my left ovary. The ovary was behaving like a putz. Still working, but it wouldn't ovulate until late into my cycle – usually on cycle day (CD) 28. Not a deal breaker but definitely a complication because my right ovary marched on like a brown noser – ovulating exactly how it should, exactly when it should, usually on cycle day 16. I had to diligently track/temp/test each month; otherwise I might miss my ovulation entirely.

2. Old boy previously took an at-home sperm analysis kit on his swimmers, and they passed with an "all is well" positive.

We were convinced DH's spermies were not the problem.

3. That meant there must be something else. Endometriosis? A deflated tube? A flat uterus?

Long story short, my doctor held off on additional, more invasive tests with me until my guy went to a legitimate urologist for testing who would send the results back to his office.

Two weeks later we found out his swimmers were just a little confused. My doc explained it as if they were directionally challenged, and they'd bang around inside me (who knows where) without heading to the golden land (my ovaries).

A putzy ovary and misguided sperm shouldn't cause infertility on their own, of course, but to be sure his guys were reaching the planned destination my doc recommended IUI. We'd start the following month.

But then that month came and went with four trips to the office because I was ovulating from The Putz and we couldn't get the timing right. Of course.

Onto Clomid and the next cycle.

Though I've heard horror stories of the side effects with Clomid I will say this: its hold on me made me want to call my mom and apologize to her for all of the jokes I ever made about menopause. Guys, it's really not that funny to be the one driving on a 70-degree day with the windows down, listening to acoustic jams (like all the cool kids do), when – out of absolutely nowhere – your internal organs feel the rage of Hell's fires. I flipped on the AC, laughed hysterically with optimism thinking this meant the meds were working while sobbing with guilt at the same time because I would make fun of my mom when her loins became a relentless inferno. Sweat beaded on my upper lip, sincere regret pooled in my heart.

TMI Alert: Time and temperature are everything when

delivering sperm for IUI because you don't want the little guys to die before they are spun, cleaned and counted. I was super nervous about the 40-minute commute during morning rush hour and what that drive would do with DH's donation to the cause. When IUI day came, we navigated the tricky situation of collecting his specimen within the correct time frame by inviting ourselves to my brother-in-law's new house. It was only 15 minutes from the doctor's office, a quick ride for me, the girl carrying my man's cum in my cleavage to keep it body temperature (alive).

Side note: Those of you who are well endowed with chesticles should thank your boobies for hiding that cup. Let's just say my middle boob appeared quite a bit larger than the girls surrounding her.

At the time of my first IUI, I geared up for my 18th tracked two-week wait. I knew what I was up against; I'd experienced suffering through stalking my calendar only to waste tests too many days early before it made sense to even use them, but nothing – and I repeat nothing – prepared me for the agony of this specific wait:

Just before I left my IUI appointment, my doctor explained there were complications with my husband's specimen and he wasn't sure they were surmountable. If this IUI didn't work, we needed to consider going straight to IVF.

Holy shit.

I realize a year and a half of infertility questions is nothing in comparison to what some strong women have suffered through, but it's certainly not a short journey either. The silver lining for me, however? My ~~pesky~~ amazing, ~~persistent~~ brilliant therapist who constantly reminded me to take care of myself through all-things-stress.

This guide is inspired by the last five years of my life and the internal work I've done so when crazy, unexpected heartbreak hands me my ass I can navigate it like a GD lady.

Though this journey is painful, I've been able to remain sane, calm and cautiously optimistic. I haven't lost my shit a single time, guys. Not once. *It's amazing what happens when you acknowledge your feelings before they boil over.* Sure, I've snapped at my Boo, I've shut out friends, and I've certainly been an angry bird when I see others announce their pregnancy.

But it never put me in a deep depression or made me tear apart the house. *So that's a victory in my eyes.*

Self-care, as my loving former psychologist trumpeted, is the reason why I don't feel like a loon, why my husband isn't scared to share his opinion, and why I've been able to retain my sense of humor through all of this – especially through the dreaded two-week wait.

Instead of thinking about the fateful day when I can finally test, I use this time to *learn* more about myself, *do* more for others and *be* more like humans I admire. It makes me feel like I'm not wasting my days sitting on the sidelines and hoping. Instead, I'm living in the moment and doing a hella good job distracting myself.

For those of you who are still with me, know this:

> *My intention with this challenge is to get your mind off the chaos for a few minutes a day. It's really that simple.*

I wish you all the success in the world because you deserve the life you want, even if you don't believe that yet.

Sending you baby dust.

XO,
Lindsay

7 RULES ON HOW TO USE THE CHALLENGE (OR NOT)

1. **Adapt this to your cycle/needs.** If there's one thing I've learned about trying to conceive, it's that none of our bodies work the same way. Our cycles are different, some of us have a 1.5WW and others might have to wait 3 weeks. If you only need challenge activities for 12 days, then you can be selective. If you need 16 or 17 days of challenge activities, check out the supplemental material in the back. I've got you all covered.

2. **Try everything once.** You might be uncomfortable. You might absolutely despise something. But you would have never known you were uncomfortable or despised it if you had you not given it a go. Don't shortchange yourself by being a slacker. It's not a good look for anyone.

3. **Check out the initialism/term dictionary.** If you're new to this journey you might not know all of the terms or initialisms I use throughout the book. I try to use context clues, but that doesn't mean I'm good at it. If you need a cheat sheet for all-terms-fertility, I've got you covered. I also add in a few others like self-talk and chakras, because I'm a real flower child.

4. **I'm a little sass-pot.** Please ignore my sass. I make jokes; I call you girlfriend and lover, and I laugh at my own expense. Surviving stressful situations has proven to me that it's okay to chuckle even when times are serious. *That's how we do here in Sass-hole City.* If that's not your style, that's okay. I hope you find a resource more aligned with your own authentic voice. You're cool, too.

5.   **Day 15**. Day 15's challenge is divided in two: for the ladies who find themselves stricken with a BFN (big fat negative) or AF (Aunt Flow), and for those who get a BFP (big fat positive). Please choose accordingly (and if you're still unsure, that's okay: start at the beginning or look at the other options available beyond day 15). There are several more self-care ideas for everyone to take on the rest of their journeys, wherever they are headed. Don't stop reading at Day 14. Get your self-care on, sisters.

6.   **Go kick ass**. Join the (free) online community (for free) created for the ladies who bought this little gem. There, you can find a partner to take this journey with you, share your insights or vent. We're all here, we all understand. Super wicked bonus points for those who find accountability partners that are on the same day of the TWW as you, but it's not mandatory. We might all bleed the same (gross) period blood, but we don't always ovulate on the same days. (*See what I mean about stupid jokes?*)

7.   **Pay it forward.** If you feel you've been helped (or hindered) by the challenge at the end of your TWW 14-Day Challenge journey, please consider leaving an Amazon review. Someone else will surely feel the same way about the little book as you and leaving your opinion will help others decide whether to pick up this passion project (or keep on, keepin' on).

Carry on, my warrior women. You have ovaries of steel for trying this, even if your ovaries actually suck and won't do what you need them to.

APPENDIX A

THE JARGON DICTIONARY

Chakras – (in Indian thought) each of the centers (there are seven) of spiritual power in the human body.

Clomid – Clomiphene (or Clomid) is a drug commonly used to treat infertility. It stimulates an increase in the amount of hormones that support the growth and release of a mature egg, helping women ovulate.

Intentional Breathing - The type of breath that occurs when you focus on inhaling and exhaling, instead of doing it naturally. This allows you to focus on the breathing and helps to diminish worry. A typical pattern of internal breathing is to inhale to the count of 4, hold the breath for a count of 2, and exhale slowly to the count of 6 or 8. Repeat this process as needed.

Self-care - Includes any intentional actions you take to care for your physical, mental, emotional and spiritual health. Self-care is unique to every person and helps with healing (trust me, I know)

Self-talk & Internal messaging – Simply put, this is the way you talk to yourself internally or your internal voice. People receive countless messages from themselves everyday showing – very clearly – how they feel about themselves. In difficult times, it's easy for our self-talk to be negative. (*I am so* *stupid. I am fat or worthless. My body doesn't work.)* However, noticing our internal messages (or self-talk) can help us change it to something more positive. (*I am kind. I am doing the best with the situation I'm in. I am strong.*)

THE INITIALISM BANK

I don't use all of these terms regularly, but they are good to have when reading and/or discussing infertility. Ladies and gents, welcome to a cheat sheet detailing commonly used initialisms and what they stand for to help you navigate online forums and groups,

May your memorization of these terms be because you're a word nerd and not because you have to use them.

AF	Aunt Flow (periods)	**HPT**	Home pregnancy test
BBT	Basal Body temperature	**ICSI**	Intracytoplasmic Sperm Insertion
BC	Birth control	**IUI**	Intrauterine Insemination
BD	Baby dancing (sex)	**IVF**	In Vitro Fertilization
BFN	Big fat negative (pregnancy test)	**MC**	miscarriage
BFP	Big fat positive (pregnancy test)	**MS**	morning sickness
CD	Cycle day	**O**	Ovulation
CM	Cervical mucus	**OB**	Obstetrician
DH – W, P, F, B	Dear husband, wife, partner, fiancé, or boyfriend	**OHSS**	Ovarian Hyper Stimulation Syndrome
DPT	Days Pass Transfer	**OI**	Ovulation Induction
DI	Donor Insemination	**OPK**	ovulation predictor test kit
DPO	Days past ovulation	**OPU**	Ovum (Egg) Pick Up

EP	Ectopic Pregnancy	**PG**	pregnant
ER	Egg Retrieval	**PCOS**	Poly Cystic Ovarian Syndrome
ET	Embryo Transfer	**POF**	Premature Ovarian Failure
EWCM	Egg White Cervical Mucus (description of cervical mucus - for many - at or around ovulation time)	**RE**	Reproductive endocrinologist
FET	Frozen Embryo Transfer (or fertilized egg transfer)	**SB**	Stillbirth
FSH	Follicle Stimulating Hormone	**SO**	Significant other
FX	Fingers Cross	**TI**	Timed Intercourse
GIFT	Gamete Intrafallopian Transfer	**TMI**	Too much information
US	Ultrasound	**TTC**	Trying to conceive

And, of course, the reason we're all here today:

2WW (or TWW) – the 2 week wait (wait after ovulation when TTC)

HOW DUDES (PARTNERS) CAN GET DOWN WITH THE TWW

Ladies, let's talk *real* talk for just a moment. We want our partners to understand our emotional reactions to this process but let's be honest, it's damn near impossible if you haven't experienced it – just like any other traumatic event in life.

It's not that they don't want to do something, and they've probably tried, but this pain runs deep and they are not equipped to take it all away.

As you progress through this challenge, I encourage you to get your partner involved and, lucky for you, I'm giving them a space to do so right here in this guide.

Welcome to the Love List, a simple way for your lover to let you know they care. Each day that you progress through the challenge, they can leave you a message of encouragement or admiration RIGHT HERE. This allows them to feel like they are involved in your process and it allows you to feel loved, appreciated and admired.

Partners, it's simple (but let's go for clear too). Your woman needs your support through this journey. Leave her a little note of encouragement for each day of this journey.
- Tell her she looked beautiful before work.
- Share how much you admire her strength.
- Remind her of why you fell in love
- Tell her something you've been meaning to say (but haven't)
- Acknowledge her feelings and tell her you care

A little goes a long way. This is the great way to be involved in the two week wait.

Rad, right?

DAY 1 DOTES:

_____

_____

DAY 2 TRIBUTES:

_____

_____

DAY 3 THANK YOUS:

_____

_____

DAY 4 FLIRTS:

_____

_____

DAY 5 FLUSTER-WORTHY PRAISES:

_____

_____

DAY 6 SERENADES:

_____

_____

DAY 7 SWEETNESS:

_____

_____

DAY 8 ENCOURAGEMENT:

_____

_____

DAY 9 NICEITIES:

_____

_____

DAY 10 TOUTS:

_____

_____

DAY 11 EXCELLENCE:

_____

_____

DAY 12 TWINKLINGS:

_____

_____

DAY 13 HAPPY THOUGHTS:

_____

_____

DAY 14 FEVERISH PRAISES:

_____

_____

DAY 1:

I TRUST MY BODY.

Though there may be complications inside of your body, it *is* what allows you to wake up erry' day. It might not be as hot or firm as you want, but you certainly wouldn't be here without it, right? Nurture yourself, appreciate each limb, and give thanks to your body for what it supplies you: a chance at life and another day to continue growing. We're so eager to point out flaws or imperfections, but we don't truly appreciate what it gives us. And that's just silly.

How can you thank your body for what it does for you? What is your favorite body part? How does it help you serve your family and society? Yourself?

_____

_____

_____

_____

TODAY'S CHALLENGE:

Walk it (read: *body gratitude*) out.

Take a short walk. While walking, use the phrase "I love my body because [enter reason here]," and fill in the blank with the first thought that comes to mind. Repeat this process every few steps until you've finished your walk. This will lift your spirits and help you appreciate what you do have.

It might feel silly, but there's nothing better than a little laughter to help you lighten up and, let's face it, today is a day when you could sure use a laugh.

Alternative: if you cannot walk far (due to weather or health restrictions), consider laying somewhere outdoors (or near a window while indoors) where you can look outside and watch the sky. Practice intentional breathing (inhale to a count of four, hold the breath for two counts, then exhale for longer than four counts). During the exhale, think the same statement, "I love my body because_____." Rinse. Repeat.

Challenge Notes:

What thought first came to mind as you walked? What came up as you continued down your path? Did anything you listed surprise you? How much more invigorated were you at the end of this practice?

Why does your body rock?

DAY 2:

I EMBRACE NEW BEGINNINGS.

The thought of starting over can sometimes feel daunting because we are so afraid all the hard work we put into our lives before a new beginning would end up being useless. Especially when it comes to trying to conceive.

However, new beginnings allow us an opportunity at gaining fresh perspectives and they also allow us to use the lessons we already learned to better our understanding of ourselves and our next steps. New beginnings? They're always necessary for growth.

What lessons have you learned when you believed no good could come from a new chapter? How can you now use this information to better yourself? What turning point in life seemed traumatic before but is now something you are thankful for?

_____

_____

_____

_____

Even something as simple as decluttering – getting rid of things that no longer serve us – can open up space for new, loving energy and calm our minds.

TODAY'S CHALLENGE:

It's time to get rid of the sh*t (mentally, emotionally, and literally). *Don't worry ladies, we aren't doing a cleanse; we're cleaning out a different kind of poo.*

Choose one space in your home, car or office that needs to be decluttered. Do you have a junk drawer in the kitchen? Is it supremely embarrassing to admit you're hoarding pens? Has your car served as a trash bin? **Now** is the time to clean one avoided, cluster-freak space because clutter has a way of making us feel stress. Let's turn that mess into a masterpiece that actually calms you.

Clean your office (or just your desk if you're a real slob), your mail bin, or your entryway (hello, shoe stash). Trust me, you'll feel clarity once the space has it.

Side note: taking before and after pictures = visible progress. That's a good thing.

Challenge Notes:

How does it feel to have a clean, fresh space? Is this a practice you could implement in your weekly/monthly routine? What messages – internal thoughts (negative or positive) - did you receive from yourself as you cleaned out the untidy space? How did you feel after you finished up?

DAY 3:

I LOVE MYSELF.

It's very easy to start feeling defective when our bodies aren't doing what we've always thought and been told they're supposed to do automatically. With hopes and dreams shattered, infertility can truly make us begin resenting our bodies, our feelings and ourselves. We can have thoughts like:

- *If my partner knew I would struggle with fertility, they would have chosen someone else.*

- *I torture myself every time I'm in the TWW. Why am I so stupid?*

- *If only I would have lost weight, produced more follicles, drank more pomegranate juice, this would've worked last time.*

Cut it out! This is the perfect time for you to begin practicing self-love and self-acceptance.

What do you bring to the Universe that serves others? How are you special? What character trait has best served you throughout your life?

_____

_____

_____

_____

TODAY'S CHALLENGE:

Write a love letter to yourself. Yes, really. Think about the qualities that make you who you are and how those things have helped you become the rad person you are. Talk to yourself with patience and kindness, share exactly what you know are the best parts of yourself. Then, once you've finished, read it back to yourself aloud.

Cherish the gratitude the writer has for the reader.

Place this letter somewhere only you can find it and read it on the days you're feeling less-than- loveable.

Remember, nobody is reading this but you so don't worry about perfect phrases or punctuation. This is an act of love, not an exam. Just write, lover. You'll be shocked at what you create.

Challenge Notes:

*Was this difficult to do? Why? What do you love about yourself and this journey? How can you remind yourself of how much love you deserve? Where can you put your love letter so you can access it whenever you need (hint: do NOT put it in that junk drawer you **just** cleaned)?*

DAY 4:

AS SADNESS DEPARTS, A RENEWED SENSE OF HOPE SETTLES IN MY HEART.

Social media has become a daily activity for so many. Between catching up with friends who've moved away and reading the latest gossip from coworkers, we're inundated with draaaama. I am a social media junkie, ya'll. Seriously, I live for this shiz.

However, stalking social media can do more harm than good. Can I get an "amen" for feeling frustration (or anger) when another friend announces her pregnancy? It's not that I'm not happy for them, but my gaping womb feels so achy and echo-y (not a real word, I know) because I want what they have.

> *What social media outlet upsets you the most? Are their specific people who send you over the edge to crazy-town? Who gets hurt if you unfollow them?*
>
> *(The last question is a trick one. Unfollowing does not equal unfriending.)*

_____

_____

_____

TODAY'S CHALLENGE:

Remove social media "friends" who trigger insecurity, anger or resentment. This can include anyone who talks nonstop about pregnancy, people who have drastically different political or religious views than you, or anyone who constantly complains and kills your vibe. Remember, you do not have to remove them as friends. Instead, you may "unfollow" their posts. This gives you the opportunity to follow them again when the time is right. (Like when the election is over).

If this task seems too overwhelming because of the sheer amount of nastiness on your page, feel free to limit yourself to 10 people and to come back and revise your setting again another day. If you do not have 10 people you'd like to unfollow, simply unfollow the few you do have (and give a shout out towards the sky in gratitude because YOU have amazing friends).

Helpful tip: I do this daily by checking out my birthday list. If someone shows up that makes me feel like turds, I simply unfollow them (because annoyance is overrated).

Challenge Notes:

How did it feel to give yourself permission to remove negativity from your life? Did the resentment towards these people release as you hid their triggering posts? How will this improve your mood?

DAY 5:

I CHOOSE HEALTHY FOODS.
I CRAVE FOODS THAT NURTURE ME.

Healthful living is a choice we can make every day. While there is nothing wrong with the occasional candy bar or date for ice cream, nourishing our bodies not only helps us along our fertility journey but it also helps us feel better. Think about it: if you love your body and provide it nutritious foods, you are giving it the best opportunity to maintain a level of health that helps you succeed in all areas of your life. That shit houses your mind and soul, friends. Take care of it!

What healthy foods do you absolutely love?
What food nourishes you and instantly gives you energy?

_____

_____

_____

_____

TODAY'S CHALLENGE:

First, take a deep breath. Cooking can feel like a chore and it might always, but we're only talking about ONE meal here.

Cook something you've never made before focusing on healthy foods you enjoy. You don't have to follow a recipe, and it doesn't have to be an elaborate dish. Simple and satiating, create a plate that will honor your body. Relish in the fact that you love yourself enough to give yourself the best meal possible.

Challenge Notes:

Write down your recipe. Did you love it? Unexpectedly hate it? How did mindfully creating a plate full of nutritious food make you feel about how you are treating yourself?

DAY 6:

A PERFECT BALANCE IS COMING TO MY BODY NOW.

A balanced body is a happy body. When we take the time to balance our chakras (See Appendix A), we are taking the time to be sure information is being sent and received efficiently up and down your spine. If one chakra is blocked, you're blocked.

Now, if you aren't woo-woo or know diddly-squat about chakras, let me give you the condensed low-down: exploring your body helps keep you grounded (and when you are grounded anxiety cannot root itself and steal your brain like a thief in the night).

Where do you feel stress in your body? Are their places along your spine where you feel joy or strength?

_____

_____

_____

_____

Today's Challenge:

Complete one of the meditations listed below. Some (or all) of them might feel a little strange if you haven't practiced meditation or studied chakras. HOWEVER, this practice – in its most simple form – is about being in the moment and turning off all outside thoughts so your brain can rest.

Please, try it.

At the very least, you're exploring new avenues that might help you throughout the rest of your life. Two meditations listed below (available at time of publication) are fertility related and you're welcome to use them, but if you'd rather not think about fertility today, the first option is for anyone; it's a simple tune-up of all of the chakra centers in your body.

Chakras: 7 minute tune-up:
(https://youtu.be/F8kwc1lkiAQ)

Fertility Meditation Through the Chakras:
(https://youtu.be/apJXGs-rts0)

For those of you who are "weirded out" by all this chakra talk:

<u>Positive Affirmations for Fertility</u>:
(<u>https://youtu.be/WDr5TaABRyg</u>)

Challenge Notes:

Did you find it difficult to shut down intruding thoughts? Do you believe trying this again might help you better focus? When is the last time you gave yourself this much time to shut down and focus? How does it feel to dedicate that much time to yourself?

DAY 7:

I AM ENERGETIC AND CHANNEL POSITIVE ENERGY.

As a former teacher and positive reinforcer: Congratulations! You've made it to Day 7 of the TWW Challenge Workbook. Half-way there, honey!

The next two days of challenge assignments go hand-in-hand.

Every day during the challenge you read a positive affirmation in bold at the top of each page. Positivity helps you overcome obstacles. Surviving domestic violence and battling through trauma recovery lead to my love of affirmations even though I said they were BS hooey when I began reading them. As I continued reading them, though, I realized I was full of far more sunshine than vinegar. Just from reading positive things!

#miracle

Are the thoughts you think about yourself more negative or positive? Are there certain times of the day (week or month) when you're more negative? Can you reframe those moments by adding new, positive affirmations into your life?

_____

_____

_____

_____

Today's Challenge:

Create your own affirmation or mantra. To do this, think about your life's journey and the one area you'd like most to heal. Then, create a positive statement about this area of your life.

For example – If you've been trying to be more authentic in your interactions (such a buzz-word, authentic), simply write a way you're more open and honest:

I honor my feelings by sharing them with my partner.

Your mantra or affirmation doesn't have to be poetic, but it does need to be personal and, yes, it can be about your journey toward parenthood or your body's ability to conceive.

If you struggle, that's okay, you're welcome to use any of the affirmations listed in this book. The TTC Challenge is called a challenge for a reason: I'm asking you to step outside of your comfort zone and experience life in a different way.

<u>Challenge Notes:</u>

How many negative thoughts came to mind before you shut them down and started creating? If you do this again, would you be able to acknowledge those negative thoughts earlier? What was the best part of creating your own affirmation?

DAY 8:

BEING CREATIVE HELPS ME FEEL JOY.

If you are skimming the book to land on random pages each day, you'll need to complete the previous day's assignment before completing this one, so scroll backward, sister.

We're stealing the beauty and power of the present when we wish away days. There are many times in life I've *wanted* to fast forward or skip ahead, but learning to become comfortable in discomfort is a life skill that has taught me that this path exists for a reason (even when it feels like total bullshit). No matter how painful it is that we can't see the future (or be in it), it's important we focus on the power that today gives us.

What lessons can you learn from being in this very moment? Is patience something you should learn? Can you give yourself permission to slow down and enjoy the journey, no matter how long or trying it has been?

_____

_____

_____

_____

Today's Challenge:

Today you will create a visual representation of yesterday's affirmation. You can do this by drawing, painting, sketching or doodling. What does the thought behind your affirmation look like? What color is it? Is it big and bold or soft and subtle? How does the visual representation of your thought remind you to take in the power of this very moment?

Your gut reactions to those questions should be what you follow, because your intuition is a gift we often overlook. If for some reason you were all, "It's red and big looks like my dad's nose," then that's what you should honor, okie-doke?

This symbol represents you and your affirmation. It doesn't need to be perfect, but heartfelt is cool.

<u>Challenge Notes:</u>

What is the most empowering element of your art? Do the curves of your symbol represent the femininity you possess? Why did you choose the color(s) you used? Where can you place this reminder of your affirmation so you can begin building those positive habits even more?

DAY 9:

I ALLOW HARMONIOUS ENERGIES TO HEAL ME IN THIS VERY MOMENT.

Be honest, this fertility journey has likely changed your sex drive and changed your energy around baby dancing and your partner. Maybe you want more and more baby dance time while your partner feels like you're using him as a means to an end. It's possible you're both feeling like sex is a total chore and you only BD when you're ovulating. Or, if you're going through treatments, you're tired of being poked and prodded and you don't want anyone else touching you.

Woof. The journey through infertility can change a lot of things in a partnership. Bringing harmony back into the bedroom will help you through this journey.

Has our sex-life changed since we began TTC? What things do you love about your sex life? What do you wish would revert back to the days when sex was something you did for pleasure and not for reproduction?

_____

_____

TODAY'S CHALLENGE:

It's simple. It's satisfying. It's seriously going to shock you. Today's challenge is to have an orgasm.

You can do this alone (*gasp*) or with your partner (*oh-la-la*). However you feel called to call out (see what I did there?), it's time to take matters into your own hands and go for the big O because – well – they feel *good*.

Not only that, there's a slew of other science-and-statistically proven benefits to orgasms, including stress relief and anti-aging. Don't believe me? Google's your go-to for proof.

If your doctor has recommended a period of pelvic rest, please do not complete this without consulting them. Instead, you can have a brain-gasm by reading something you love or watching a new documentary OR you can give your partner an orgasm, but I really don't consider that self-care so much as a gift (teehee). Remember, you can always look in the back of the book for a different self-care practice to use.

Challenge Notes:

I'm just leaving this here for you to write about your day, your deed, and when you did that damn thing. I bet you put Meg Ryan to shame. *Winky face emoji*

DAY 10:

I RELY ON THE POWER OF NOW.

As we get closer and closer to the day you're able to test, it's easier and easier to get more focused on what's to come.

You will never be more powerful than the day you realize you can rely on the power of now. *I know I've already said this but it's SO important.*

Today is a day you know you have. It's the time that has been granted to you and a moment you should relish. Instead of thinking ahead, show gratitude for *this* day, *this* moment, *this* beautiful, and sacred life you have.

Repeat: If I did not have today, I could not have my future. I appreciate today for what it is giving me, and I love today for the lessons and growth it provides. I rely on the power of now.

> *What can you do today that you've been putting off for days (or even years)? How can you show the world gratitude for another chance at life?*

_____

_____

_____

_____

TODAY'S CHALLENGE:

You have several options for things you can complete today. Please choose one item, but you may complete more if you feel compelled, just remember to avoid overwhelming yourself. The point of these activities is to keep yourself present and engaged, not to add stress to your life.

Options:

- Scratch one forever-on-the-list item off your to-do list. *Nobody likes a lurking item.*
- Do one thing you love doing: read, dance, grab lunch with a friend, call your mom
- Give: to a charity, to a donation center, your time/ear/hand
- Wake up early and enjoy a moment of solitude in the morning, watch the sunrise and be thankful for what you're witnessing.

<u>*Challenge Notes:*</u>

How did you embrace the now? What perspective did you gain that you wouldn't have if you refused to participate in today's challenge? What was the best part of my day?

DAY 11:

I AM GROWING MORE POSITIVE BY THE DAY.

You have dedicated yourself to exploring and nurturing your own power for the last eleven days. Though it might seem a long journey, it's important to acknowledge your personal growth as you proceed. You can do this!

It's a day of wild gratitude and uproarious validation.

How have you witnessed your own strength over the last week and a half? In what ways have you been more positive each day? Have you been open-minded about the challenge activities?

_____

_____

_____

_____

TODAY'S CHALLENGE:

I had an uber crush on Dick Van Dyke when I was little after seeing *Mary Poppins*. It wasn't that I thought he was dreamy or age-appropriate but, instead, his joy was infectious. In fact, my favorite song for my entire childhood was "I Love To Laugh" from *Mary Poppins*.

Today, you're going to laugh. Here are a few ways to get there:

- Watch a sitcom you love but haven't seen in forever
- Tell silly jokes to friends, family or coworkers and feed off of their giggles
- Get on YouTube and watch a comedian, cat videos, or something that seems funny to you, but do this with someone else because their laughter will a catalyst.
- Reminisce about funny happenings with another person who was there
- Dress your pet (or partner) in a silly outfit

Even though I don't dream of Mr. Van Dyke anymore, I laugh about this little known fact often. It's balm on hard days, literally the best medicine.

<u>Challenge Notes:</u>

What made you giggle? Was it easier than you anticipated? How can you add laughter to your daily routine as a self-care practice?

DAY 12:

I PAY ATTENTION TO THE WORDS I HEAR

Listening is a skill we often take for granted, especially when we feel isolated or misunderstood. Too often we want others to listen to our worries and us without truly understanding the power of words. When you listen, you download insights into life and love. You become a more complete and better person simply by using a given skill in a new way.

> *How can listening to something improve your outlook? Do you normally rush through the day without paying enough attention to the internal conversations you're having? Who can you talk to that will help you better your listening abilities?*

_____

_____

_____

_____

TODAY'S CHALLENGE:

Yes, we are focusing on listening today, but we're also tapping into your own creativity and imagination. Today is the best day to find your favorite uplifting album and listen to it (all of it). Music can heal you. It inspires, evokes happiness, and – sometimes – makes you want to dance.

Find your favorite feel good music, dim the lights and light a candle. Give yourself time to absorb the messages you hear. Or, if you want, get your groove on and celebrate the simplicity of finding joy in something you already have.

Bonus points if you do this in the morning. It'll set the tone for your whole day.

Challenge Notes:

Why did you choose the album you did? How did it make you feel? What genre of music can you listen to on hard days?

DAY 13:

"ALMOST EVERYTHING WILL WORK AGAIN
IF YOU UNPLUG IT FOR A FEW MINUTES,
EVEN YOU." ~~ ANNE LAMOTT

Distractions show up unannounced when we're already preoccupied. Our phones are constantly buzzing, our computers are constantly on... But when we unplug from the very things that keep our minds racing, we are better able to feel our own emotions while honoring them.

Which social media outlets suck me in each day? Instead of instantly grabbing for my phone, whom can I talk to or what activity can I do that will keep me off of my computer and other electronic devices?

_____

_____

_____

_____

Today's challenge:

Stay off social media, news media outlets or anything that serves as a time-filler. Instead, fill your day with meaningful, helpful activities making you feel like the highest and best version of yourself.

Fill your time with things like:

- Bake a dessert and give it to a neighbor, friend or family member who needs it (or take it to them and chat about what's going on in their lives).
- Color. Target has coloring books for REAL cheap.
- Spend time outdoors doing something you love, bird or babe watching are a-okay.
- Do gentle exercise like yoga
- Repeat one of the previous day's activities that truly spoke to you/helped you feel good
- Reflect via gratitude list, refocusing your emotions on all of the positive things that happened today.

<u>Challenge Notes:</u>

What 10 things am I most grateful for today?

DAY 14:

MY PARTNER IS THE LOVE OF MY LIFE AND MY WORLD'S CENTER. JUST AS I LOVE HIM/HER, HE/SHE LOVES ME EQUALLY.

This journey is tough. Resentment, frustration, and feelings of unworthiness creep in without warning. Although these thoughts are hard to face, this journey would be even harder without the love and support of your partner. Even though they may never know exactly how this experience feels for you, they too are dealing with their own doubts and depression.

When you signed on for this relationship, you did it because you thought the person you loved was worthy of your attention.

What has your partner done for you to help you through this often painful process? What qualities does your partner possess that made you fall in love with them? What have you learned about your partner that has deepened your connection?

TODAY'S CHALLENGE:

Write your partner a love note, poem, or make them a card.

Infertility can make even the strongest couples a bit weaker, but that doesn't mean your bond is permanently damaged. Though you've been attempting to give yourself and your future baby a lot of love, maybe it's time you give it to the person who's riding shotgun through the storm.

Tell them why you love them, why you're thankful to have them, and why – no matter what happens – you're thankful to call them yours. Since we're at the end of the TWW, their nerves and anxieties will be just as high as yours. Help them through this time by giving them a piece of your soul on paper.

<u>Challenge Notes:</u>

Why do you love your partner? How have their inspiration notes through this challenge made you feel? If you could say one thing to your partner without feeling vulnerable, what would it be?

DAY 15 (BFN):

EVERY TIME MY PERIOD COMES I REJOICE IN THE FACTTHAT MY BODY IS FUNCTIONING CORRECTLY.

Things didn't go as planned. You're frustrated, heartbroken and maybe even unsurprised by Aunt Flow's arrival. Or maybe you're here because you already tested and got a BFN. While disappointment is justified while you're TTC, it's time for a little perspective:

- Each of us struggles in our own way but the pain we feel is unanimous.

- What would you want your best friend to know about themselves when they are at their lowest? Can you treat yourself the same?

- There is no harm in feeling pain or grieving. There is not one right way to navigate this road.

Instead of forgetting about all of the hard work you've put into the last two weeks, please remember that today – of all days – is likely when you need self-care most. Plus, you still deserve it.

You are worthy. You are loved. You are a gift in the lives of those who know you.

Please don't drop the ball because you feel like your heart is shattered. Take a minute, a break, a long breath and accept what has happened. Then take care of you.

What did I learn about myself over the last two weeks that will make my next cycle easier to navigate? What tools did I love that I plan to use again this month?

_____

_____

_____

_____

TODAY'S CHALLENGE:

Make self-care your choice. Do something that makes you feel powerful or healthy or happy. Whatever it is, do it with the intention of helping yourself cope with parts of life that feel unfair.

For me, this has always been a good day for a glass of wine and a pedicure.

A few ideas include:

- Spa-like activities, whether at home or in a salon
- More decluttering. Revamp your closet, your book shelves, your makeup bag or paint collection
- Dig in the dirt. Have you considered a hope garden? A hope plant? Have you neglected your already existing flowers?
- Read a book of your choosing, watch a movie you haven't seen in years, listen to that album you love
- Nap

Challenge Notes:

Even though today didn't go as you wanted, how can you take care of yourself? How can you make sure your needs are met? Have you acknowledged and accepted your feelings? Can you, at the very least, share one good thing that happened today (even if it's as simple as waking up or receiving a hug)?

DAY 15 (BFP):

MY CHOICES THROUGHOUT PREGNANCY ARE NOT BASED ON FEAR, BUT – INSTEAD - ON FACT.

First, congratulations! You received a great gift via positive pregnancy test, one you've been waiting for (no matter how many TWWs you've endured). Yet, here we go: another round of *what if* and *is that normal* questions that could lead you down a million paths to self-destruction. They key to self-care, my friends, is not that you only use it in times of crisis or concern, but also at the height of happiness. To make it a habit, you must continue to take care of YOU. The best part of this commitment, especially now, is that you're teaching your unborn babe the skills it'll need to navigate the world. The healthiest pregnancy possible only happens when you take care of yourself, gorgeous. Don't forget that.

How can I ensure I'm taking care of myself mentally, emotionally, physically, and/or spiritually during this pregnancy? When scary days or happy days arise, how can I remind myself that self-care is still vital?

_____

_____

_____

_____

TODAY'S CHALLENGE:

Make self-care your choice. Do something that makes you feel powerful or healthy or happy. Whatever it is, do it with the intention of helping yourself cope with parts of life that feel unknown.

A few ideas include:

- Plan the moment you tell your husband or family that you're expecting
- Create a plan for yourself for the days when you're emotionally or physically drained
- Spa-like activities, whether at home or in a salon
- More decluttering. Revamp your closet, your book shelves, your makeup bag or paint collection
- Sit in the park and people watch
- Read a book of your choosing, watch a movie you haven't seen in years, listen to that album you love
- Nap

Challenge Notes:

Even now that you have an answer you wanted, how can you take care of yourself? How can you make sure your needs are met?

MORE SELF-CARE PRACTICES FOR DAILY LIFE:

- Create and keep a gratitude journal. Write a list daily.

- Ground yourself by eating something salty, sour or sweet when overwhelmed by emotion. The body's reaction helps you focus on something else while feeling debilitated.

- Find and join a local (or online) support group where you can listen and share.

- Take up a new hobby you've been interested in. Ballroom dancing, photography, or knitting?

- Have one caffeinated or alcoholic beverage since you've been holding off during your TWW, but don't consume so much you feel guilty, buzzy, or hung over.

- Research a book full of positive affirmations that will take you through an entire year. Call a friend, hug your partner, and recognize that it's okay to ask for support sometimes.

- Meditate (using the resources provided here or others that work for you).

- Get a facial.

- Start learning about the theory or practice that has piqued your interest.

- Go on a date with your partner.

- Go to a museum, show or sporting event of interest.

- Create your own list of self-care practices that you think will help you through the next TWW. Write about your experience so others know they aren't alone.

- List the reasons you love life, your job, your family or friends.

- Recognize how much further along you are on this path, even if it feels like you haven't moved at all.

- Acknowledge every emotion but don't let it hold you hostage.

- Check out Brené Brown's work on vulnerability,

shame and grief. Watch TEDx talks that inspire you to be a better human.

- Find quotes that stir your soul and provoke inspired happiness, even when you're alone.

- Stay determined, stay persistent, STAY IN YOUR LANE, and stay the amazing, powerful and brave woman you are. This journey isn't easy, but you're trying to do it with grace and poise, two things many people simply choose not to do.

THE TWW CHALLENGE: NOTES FOR A SASSY GIRL TO REMEMBER (FOR NEXT TIME YOU'RE TTC)

MEET THE AUTHOR

Lindsay Fischer graduated from Missouri State University with a Bachelor of Science in secondary education, English. An avid reader and learner, Lindsay took her passion for words into a classroom before starting a career in writing. Life got messy when she fell in love with a man who would become her abuser, and it pulled her from the classroom. After three years of trauma therapy, she saw an opportunity to use her voice against domestic violence, blogging under the pseudonym Sarafina Bianco since 2009. She revealed her real identity in 2015 when her memoir, *The House on Sunset*, was re-released.

Since then Lindsay has continued advocating for causes that are close to her heart. Her most recent work details her struggles with infertility.

She believes, more than anything else, women feel alone and unheard when they're dealing with life's challenges. Through sharing her own stories she's found a support system and rid herself of shame. Lindsay wants that for everyone.

You can find her weekly ramblings on her website, http://survivorswillbeheard.com or chat with her on

Twitter every Monday night at 9pm EST during #domesticviolencechat

Her memoir, *The House on Sunset,* is available on Amazon.

She currently lives with her husband and three other dudes (all dogs) in St. Louis, MO.

Made in the USA
Middletown, DE
17 January 2021